Get the Message

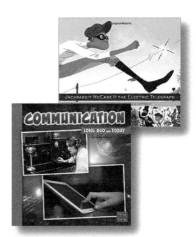

Description

Students read a tall tale featuring the invention of the electric telegraph, learn how to decipher Morse code, and explore the influence of the telegraph and various other communication innovations over time. Then they design a solution that uses sound or light to communicate over a distance and compare the strengths and weaknesses of each.

Alignment With the *Next Generation Science Standards*

Performance Expectations

1-PS4-4: Use tools and materials to design and build a device that uses light or sound to solve the problem of communicating over a distance.

K-2-ETS1-3: Analyze data from tests of two objects designed to solve the same problem to compare the strengths and weaknesses of how each performs.

Science and Engineering Practices	Disciplinary Core Ideas	Crosscutting Concept
Constructing Explanations and Designing Solutions Use tools and materials provided to design a device that solves a specific problem. **Engaging in Argument from Evidence** Make a claim about the effectiveness of an object, tool, or solution that is supported by relevant evidence.	**PS4.C: Information Technologies and Instrumentation** People also use a variety of devices to communicate (send and receive information) over long distances. **ETS1.C: Optimizing the Design Solution** Because there is always more than one possible solution to a problem, it is useful to compare and test designs.	**Patterns** Patterns in the natural and human-designed world can be observed, used to describe phenomena, and used as evidence.

Note: The activities in this lesson will help students move toward the performance expectations listed, which is the goal after multiple activities. However, the activities will not by themselves be sufficient to reach the performance expectations.

Featured Picture Books

TITLE: **Jackrabbit McCabe and the Electric Telegraph**
AUTHOR: **Lucy Margaret Rozier**
ILLUSTRATOR: **Leo Espinosa**
PUBLISHER: **Schwartz & Wade**
YEAR: **2015**
GENRE: **Story**
SUMMARY: *Jackrabbit McCabe's unusually long legs have made him the fastest thing around, and he uses his speed for everything from racing against horses to fetching the doctor. But when the electric telegraph arrives in Windy Flats, Jackrabbit may have met his match.*

TITLE: **Communication: Long Ago and Today**
AUTHOR: **Lindsy O'Brien**
PUBLISHER: **Capstone Press**
YEAR: **2013**
GENRE: **Non-Narrative Information**
SUMMARY: *Simple text and photographs describe the history of communication technologies, from ancient hieroglyphics to the computers of today.*

Time Needed

This lesson will take several class periods. Suggested scheduling is as follows:

Session 1: **Engage** with *Jackrabbit McCabe and the Electric Telegraph* Read-Aloud and **Explore** with Crack the Code

Session 2: **Explain** with Card Sequencing and *Communication: Long Ago and Today* Read-Aloud

Session 3: **Elaborate** with Get the Message Design Challenge

Session 4: **Evaluate** with Comparing Devices

Materials

For Card Sequencing

- Communication Innovation Cards (1 uncut set per pair of students)
- Sentence strips (optional, 2 per pair)
- Glue (optional)

For Get the Message Design Challenge

- Various materials to build a communication device that uses *light*, such as the following:
  - Flashlights, finger lights, and so on
  - Construction paper or index cards
  - Scissors
  - Opaque plastic cup

National Science Teaching Association

- Various materials to build a communication device that uses *sound*, such as the following:
  - Coffee cans (Cover sharp edges with duct tape or masking tape.)
  - Different-sized plastic cups
  - Pencils, spoons, and so on
  - Bells
  - Plastic eggs to fill with rice, beans, or popcorn
  - Coins and rubber bands to make homemade finger cymbals

Student Pages

- Morse Code Key (½ page, cut out)
- Crack the Code
- Communication Innovation Cards
- Get the Message Design Challenge
- Evaluating Your Design
- STEM Everywhere

Background for Teachers

In 1837, the *electric telegraph* was patented in the United States by American artist and inventor Samuel Morse. Before the telegraph, most messages sent over a distance were handwritten and had to be delivered on horseback. It could take days to carry a message a long distance. The telegraph allowed messages to be sent over great distances almost instantly by sending electrical pulses through wires. To send a telegraph, a handwritten message would be carried to a telegraph operator, who would then translate it into *Morse code,* a series of dots and dashes. The operator would tap the code on the telegraph, which would send electrical impulses through a wire to the receiving operator's location. There, the pulses were recorded as dots and dashes on a thin strip of paper. The receiving operator would translate the message from Morse code back into words, and that written message (called a *telegram*) would be delivered.

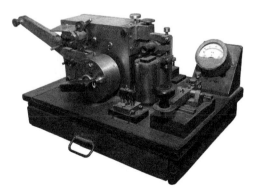

ELECTRIC TELEGRAPH

Telegraphs could even be sent across the ocean, after undersea cables were laid along the ocean floor. Newspapers, railroads, and government agencies used most telegraph wires, but the public also used them to share important personal news over long distances, such as marriages, births, and deaths. People would pay by the word to send a telegram, so the messages were usually short. The invention of the telegraph revolutionized communication. At last, people had a way to learn of important events soon after they happened. Although no longer widely used today, Morse code is still used by amateur radio operators and helps some people with disabilities communicate. The invention of the telegraph began the telecommunication age and led to many more innovations, such as the telephone. In the 1870s, inventor Alexander Graham Bell found a way

to use a telegraph wire to send the sound of his voice. By the late 1800s, wires connected major cities around the world.

In this lesson, students learn about the telegraph's significant influence on society and how it paved the way for many other communication innovations. They read about the history of communication, from cave paintings to telephones to smartphones. Then they are challenged to design and build devices that use light or sound to communicate over a distance and compare the strengths and weaknesses of those devices. In this design challenge, students are engaged in the science and engineering practice (SEP) of constructing explanations and designing solutions. They also use the SEP of engaging in argument from evidence as they make a claim about the effectiveness of their solution that is supported by evidence. Students explore the crosscutting concept (CCC) of patterns in the designed world as they recognize the pattern of improvements in communication devices over time.

Learning Progressions

Below are the disciplinary core idea (DCI) grade band endpoints for grades K–2 and 3–5. These are provided to show how student understanding of the DCIs in this lesson will progress in future grade levels.

DCIs	Grades K–2	Grades 3–5
PS4.C: Information Technologies and Instrumentation	• People use a variety of devices to communicate (send and receive information) over long distances.	• Digitized information can be transmitted over long distances without significant degradation. High-tech devices, such as computers or cell phones, can receive and decode information—convert it from digitized to voice—and vice versa.
ETS1.C: Optimizing the Design Solution	• Because there is always more than one possible solution to a problem, it is useful to compare and test designs.	• Different solutions need to be tested in order to determine which of them best solves the problem, given the criteria and the constraints.

Source: Willard, T., ed. (2015). *The NSTA quick-reference guide to the* NGSS: *Elementary school.* Arlington, VA: NSTA Press.

engage

Jackrabbit McCabe and the Electric Telegraph Read-Aloud

Connecting to the Common Core
Reading: Literature
KEY IDEAS AND DETAILS: 1.1

*Inferring*

Show students the cover of *Jackrabbit McCabe and the Electric Telegraph* and introduce the author, Lucy Margaret Rozier, and illustrator, Leo Espinosa. *Ask*

? From looking at the cover and reading the title, what do you think this book is about? (Students might infer that some sort of race is going on and that the wires on the cover have something to do with the electric telegraph.)

? Have you ever heard of an electric telegraph? What do you think it does? (Answers will vary.)

Questioning

Read the book aloud. Then *ask*

? Do you think this book is fiction or nonfiction? (Fiction, because a man could not run as fast as a train or grow that fast.)

Explain that this story is a type of fiction story called a *tall tale*. A tall tale is a story that is told as if it were true but has exaggerated elements. Tall tales usually center around a main character who has unbelievable abilities. Students may be familiar with tall tales about Johnny Appleseed, Pecos Bill, Paul Bunyan, or John Henry. *Ask*

? Who is the main character in this story? (Jackrabbit McCabe)

? What unbelievable ability does he have? (to run incredibly fast—faster than horses and trains)

Explain that tall tales often also include some parts that are true. In this case, the invention of the electric telegraph really did happen, and it dramatically changed the speed at which people could communicate.

explore

Crack the Code

Read the Author's Note on page 31 about the invention of the telegraph and Morse code. Here, the author explains how a telegraph operator would tap out words in Morse code, which were sent as electrical pulses through a wire. On the other end of the wire, another person would change the codes into a written message called a *telegram*.

Tell students that they are going to have the opportunity to use Morse code to decode a message. Give each student the Crack the Code student page and the Morse Code Key (½ page sheet). Model how to use the key by deciphering the first word together. Then, have students use the code to figure out the rest of the message. The deciphered message should read, "You got the message." Explain that this process mirrors what a telegraph operator

would have to do when he or she *received* a message: The operator would translate the dots and dashes into words.

Next, tell students that the first thing a telegraph operator would need to do to *send* a message would be to take a written message and translate it into Morse code. Have students write their own messages using Morse code. Tell them that most telegrams were short because people who sent them had to pay by the word! Encourage them to keep their messages to five words or less. They must first write the message out on a separate piece of paper and then translate it into Morse code on the student page. This task can be challenging, so you may want to show students the Morse Code Translator from Scout Life (see "Website" section) as an online tool to help them create their messages. The students can type in their letters, and the machine will show the Morse code. After students have completed their messages, they can trade with another student to decipher each other's messages.

USING MORSE CODE

After all students have had a chance to both decode a message and write their own messages in Morse code, *ask*

? Did you think it was easy or hard to use Morse code? (Answers will vary.)

? Was it harder to decipher a message with the code or write a message with the code? (Answers will vary.)

? What do you think it would have been like to be a telegraph operator? (Answers will vary.)

explain

Card Sequencing

 **Questioning**

> **Connecting to the Common Core**
> **Reading: Informational Text**
> KEY IDEAS AND DETAILS: 1.3

Ask

? What does it mean to communicate? (to share information or ideas with other people)

? In what ways do people communicate? (talking, facial expressions, writing notes, texting, talking on the phone, etc.)

? How do you most often communicate with people when you are far apart? (phone, text messages, e-mail, FaceTime, Skype, etc.)

? Imagine a time when there were no phones, no computers, and no electricity. How would you have communicated with people when you were not with them? (Answers will vary.)

Show students the cover of *Communication: Long Ago and Today* and introduce the author, Lindsy O'Brien. Tell students that this book is going to take them through the history of communication so they can see how drastically it has changed over the years.

Give each pair of students an uncut set of Communication Innovation Cards. Explain that an *innovation* is a new idea, device, or method of doing something. As long as humans have been communicating, we have been trying to come up with better ways to do it. Each of the cards represents an innovation that changed the way people communicate. Explain that before you read, you would like the students to cut out the cards and place the innovations in order from earliest to most recent. Tell them that if they are not familiar with all of the innovations, it is OK to make their best

guess using the pictures on the cards. Explain that they will learn about each innovation from the book and that, after the read-aloud, they will have a chance to reorder the cards. When students are finished sorting, *ask*

? What do you think was the earliest communication innovation?

? What do you think is the most recent innovation?

? Did you think this activity was easy or difficult?

? Were there any innovations you were not familiar with?

Communication: Long Ago and Today Read-Aloud

Read the book aloud, discussing how each innovation made communication faster, more efficient, and more accessible to more people.

 Card Sequencing (After Reading)

After reading, have students go back to the Communication Innovation Cards and use what they learned to reorder the cards. Using the timeline on page 19, go through the correct sequence together. The correct order is as follows:

1. Cave Paintings
2. Paper
3. Printing Press
4. Pony Express
5. Telegraph
6. Telephone
7. Radio
8. Television
9. Internet
10. Smartphone

> **CCC: Patterns**
> Patterns in the human-designed world can be observed, used to describe phenomena, and used as evidence.

You may want to have students color the cards and glue them in the correct order on sentence strips so they can display their work in the classroom.

Turn and Talk

Ask

? Now that we have the innovations in order, do you notice any pattern to the innovations? (Answers will vary but may include that each innovation improved on the one before, communication became faster with each innovation, communication became clearer with each innovation, communication became more accessible with each innovation, and so on.)

? What communication innovations do you think will come next? (Answers will vary.)

elaborate

Get the Message Design Challenge

Tell students that for hundreds of years, people have been using light and sound to send messages over distances, because sound and light can travel fast and far. For example, in ancient times, people would communicate by banging out specific rhythms on drums. These rhythms would relay messages to people far away. Before satellite communication, sailors used light to communicate with people on other ships. Bright signal lights would be used to send messages in Morse code by opening

A COMMUNICATION DEVICE

and closing shutters on the light. Short pulses of light represented the dots, and longer pulses of light represented the dashes.

> **SEP: Constructing Explanations and Designing Solutions**
> Use tools and materials provided to design a device that solves a specific problem.

Tell students that they are going to have the opportunity to use the design process to design and build a device that sends messages using codes. They will each work with a partner to design a device that uses either light or sound to send messages. Give each student the Get the Message Design Challenge student pages. Although they will be working in pairs, all students will need their own student pages. Explain the challenge, and show students the materials and tools you are providing. Encourage "out-of-the-box" thinking by asking students to consider other classroom materials that might be used. Have them follow along as you read the instructions on the student page. Brainstorm some possible designs together, such as the following:

Light

* A flashlight or finger light with construction paper or an index card that can cover the light to make patterns
* A flashlight or finger light in an opaque plastic cup with the bottom partially cut to make a flap

Sound

* A cup or coffee can that could be hit with a pencil or spoon to make different patterns
* A bell that could be rung in different patterns
* A plastic egg that could be filled with rice, beans, or popcorn to make a rattling sound
* Finger cymbals made out of rubber bands and coins

Have students decide what kind of device they want to design and circle *light* or *sound*. Next, they will come up with a design and draw it. You will need to sign off on their design drawing (Teacher

COMMUNICATING WITH LIGHT

COMMUNICATING WITH SOUND

Checkpoint under step 1 on the student page) before they begin building. Students can now use the materials provided to build their devices. Once they finish building, they can write their codes. You will need to sign off on their codes (Teacher Checkpoint under step 3) before they test their device. Encourage students to keep their codes fairly simple. For example, two taps means "raise your hand," and three taps means "jump up." Once their codes are approved, they can test their design, recording their results in the Trial 1 column of the table.

> **SEP: Engaging in Argument From Evidence**
> Make a claim about the effectiveness of a solution that is supported by relevant evidence.

Students then give the device a rating from "Didn't Work" to "Worked Great" based on evidence of its effectiveness and explain why they gave it that rating. Next, the partners discuss how to improve their design, make any agreed changes, then trade places and repeat the test, recording their results in the Trial 2 column. Finally, students rate the device again and explain their rating.

evaluate

Comparing Devices

> Connecting to the Common Core
> **Writing**
> RESEARCH TO BUILD AND PRESENT KNOWLEDGE: 1.8

National Science Teaching Association

✎ *Writing*

After students have completed the design challenge, give them each a copy of the Evaluating Your Design student page. On this page, they will evaluate whether their device would work under different conditions and list the strengths and weaknesses of their device in the table provided. Then they will compare the strengths and weaknesses of their design with another pair's device. Finally, they will share what changes they would make to their device or code if they had the opportunity to redesign one more time.

STEM Everywhere

Give students the STEM Everywhere student page as a way to involve their families and extend their learning. They can do the following activity with an adult helper and share their results with the class. If students do not have access the internet at home, you may choose to have them complete this activity at school.

Opportunities for Differentiated Instruction

This box lists questions and challenges related to the lesson that students may select to research, investigate, or innovate. Students may also use the questions as examples to help them generate their own questions. These questions can help you move your students from the teacher-directed investigation to engaging in the science and engineering practices in a more student-directed format.

Extra Support

For students who are struggling to meet the lesson objectives, provide a question and guide them in the process of collecting research or helping them design procedures or solutions.

Extensions

For students with high interest or who have already met the lesson objectives, have them choose a question (or pose their own question), conduct their own research, and design their own procedures or solutions.

After selecting one of the questions in this box or formulating their own questions, students can individually or collaboratively make predictions, design investigations or surveys to test their predictions, collect evidence, devise explanations, design solutions, or examine related resources. They can communicate their findings through a science notebook, at a poster session or gallery walk, or by producing a media project.

Research

Have students brainstorm researchable questions:

? How is Morse code still used today?

? Who invented the printing press, and how did it change communication?

? What did the first cell phones look like, and how have they changed over the years?

Continued

Opportunities for Differentiated Instruction (continued)

Investigate

Have students brainstorm testable questions to be solved through science or math:

? Which materials are best for making a string-and-cup telephone?

? What is the longest distance you can send a clear message using a string-and-cup telephone?

? Survey your friends and family: How do they get news? Radio? Television? Newspaper? Internet? Graph the results, then analyze your graph. What can you conclude?

Innovate

Have students brainstorm problems to be solved through engineering:

? Can you make a "telephone" from two cups and a string?

? Can you and a friend design a code to send secret messages to each other?

? Can you design a stand to hold a cell phone?

Website

 Morse Code Translator from *Scout Life*
https://scoutlife.org/hobbies-projects/
funstuff/575/morse-code-translator

More Books to Read

Kalman, B. 2014. *Communication: Then and now.* New York: Crabtree Publishing.
Summary: Part of the *From Olden Days to Modern Ways in Your Community* series, this book explores the various ways people communicate and how these ways have changed over time.

Maurer, T. 2019. *Samuel Morse: That's who! The story of the telegraph and Morse code.* New York: Henry Holt and Co.
Summary: This charming picture book biography of Samuel Morse tells the story of how he helped invent the telegraph as well as the system of dots and dashes that allowed for the simple transmission of messages across telegraph lines.

Yates, V. 2008. *Communication.* Chicago: Heinemann.
Summary: Part of the *Then and Now* series, this book uses simple text and photographs to compare communication methods from long ago with today's communication technologies.

Morse Code Key

A	● –	J	● – – –	S	● ● ●
B	– ● ● ●	K	– ● –	T	–
C	– ● – ●	L	● – ● ●	U	● ● –
D	– ● ●	M	– –	V	● ● ● –
E	●	N	– ●	W	● – –
F	● ● – ●	O	– – –	X	– ● ● –
G	– – ●	P	● – – ●	Y	– ● – –
H	● ● ● ●	Q	– – ● –	Z	– – ● ●
I	● ●	R	● – ●		

Morse Code Key

A	● –	J	● – – –	S	● ● ●
B	– ● ● ●	K	– ● –	T	–
C	– ● – ●	L	● – ● ●	U	● ● –
D	– ● ●	M	– –	V	● ● ● –
E	●	N	– ●	W	● – –
F	● ● – ●	O	– – –	X	– ● ● –
G	– – ●	P	● – – ●	Y	– ● – –
H	● ● ● ●	Q	– – ● –	Z	– – ● ●
I	● ●	R	● – ●		

Name: _____

Crack the Code

1. Use the Morse Code Key to decode the message below.

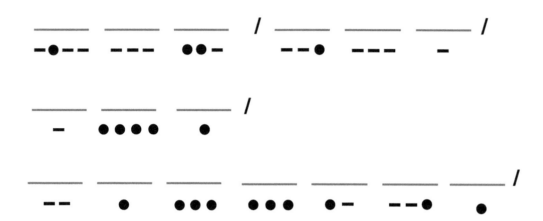

2. Now write your own message in Morse code!

   a. Write your message out on a separate piece of paper.

   b. Use the Morse Code Key to write it in Morse code below. Use a slash "/" to separate words.

   c. Trade with a friend, and figure out each other's messages.

National Science Teaching Association

Communication Innovation Cards

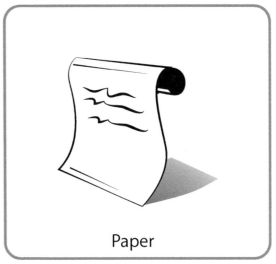

Smartphone

Paper

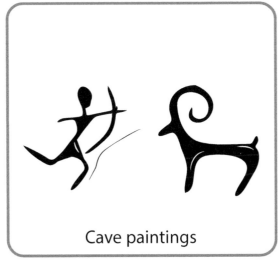

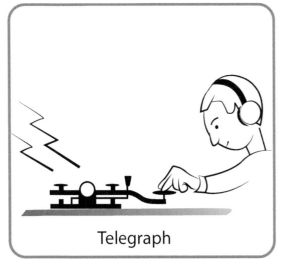

Cave paintings

Telegraph

Printing press

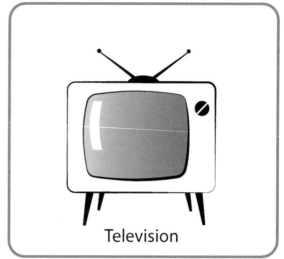

Television

Pony Express

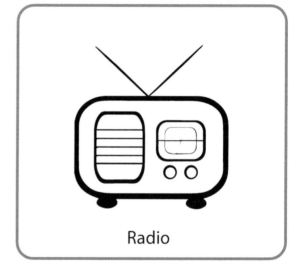

Radio

Internet

Telephone

14

Name: _____

Get the Message Design Challenge

Challenge: Design a device to communicate over a distance using light or sound.

Circle one:

Light 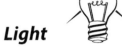   *Sound*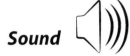

Step 1: Design the Device

Labeled Drawing

Teacher Checkpoint _____

Step 2: Build the Device

Build your device. You will need to figure out a way to send these messages to your partner:

- Raise your hand.
- Jump up.
- Touch the ground.

Step 3: Create the Codes

Together, create simple codes to send the messages across the room to your partner.

Message	Code	Trial 1 Record ✓ or ✗	Trial 2 Record ✓ or ✗
Raise your hand			
Jump up			
Touch the ground			

When you are finished creating the codes, signal your teacher.

Teacher Checkpoint _____

Step 4: Test the Device—Trial 1

One of you will use the codes to send the messages across the room to your partner. Do not send them in order.

Record your results: Put a checkmark ✓ in the **Trial 1** column above if it works or an ✗ if it doesn't work.

Step 5: Rate Your Device (circle one)

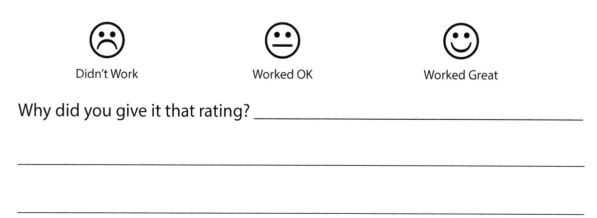

Why did you give it that rating? _____

_____

_____

National Science Teaching Association

Step 6: Improve Your Design

Based on your first test, discuss how to improve your design. Should you modify your device, use it in a different way, change your code, or make a completely different device? Then make the changes you agreed on.

Labeled Drawing of Improved Device

Step 7: Test the Device—Trial 2

Trade jobs with your partner, repeat the test, and record your results in the **Trial 2** column of the chart.

Step 8: Rate Your Device Again (circle one)

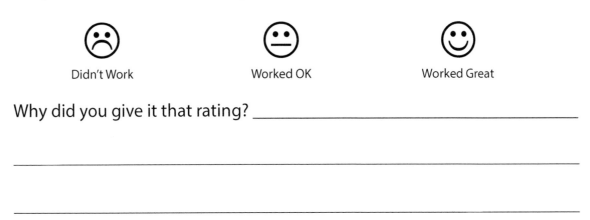

Didn't Work   Worked OK   Worked Great

Why did you give it that rating? _____

_____

_____

Name: _____

Evaluating Your Design

1. Would your design work if …

	Yes	No
the room was dark?		
the room was loud?		
you couldn't see your partner?		
you wanted to send a secret message?		

2. What are the strengths and weaknesses of your design?

Strengths	Weaknesses

3. Find another pair that used a different design. Compare the strengths and weaknesses of your design with the strengths and weaknesses of that pair's design.

4. If you had the chance to redesign your device or code, what would you change? Draw and write your ideas.

National Science Teaching Association

Name: _____

STEM Everywhere

Dear Families,

At school, we have been learning about the science and engineering behind **communication.** We have studied how messages were sent by telegraph using Morse code and how communication has changed over the years. To find out more, ask your learner the following questions and discuss their answers:

- What did you learn?

- What was your favorite part of the lesson?

- What are you still wondering?

At home, you can use an interactive website called Technology Over Time, which explores the innovations in technology since 1900.

 To explore the website, scan the QR code, search "PBS Tech Over Time," or go to *www.pbslearningmedia.org/resource/ate10.sci. engin.design.techovertime/technology-over-time.*

You can scroll through the years by dragging the rectangle across the timeline. Then you can interview a parent, a grandparent, or an adult friend to see how technology has changed in their lifetime!

Person's Name: _____ Year Born: _____

When you were younger, how did you do the following?

1. Listen to music: _____

2. Communicate with your friends: _____

3. Do your homework: _____

4. Enjoy your favorite shows: _____